When I'm Feelin
HAPPY

Written and illustrated by Trace Moroney

The Five Mile Press

When I'm feeling happy
I feel B⌢B⌢BOUNCY
and full of joy.

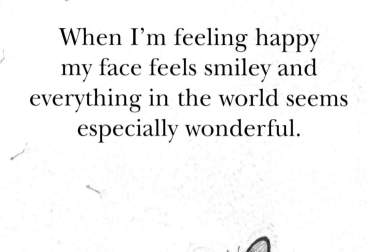

When I'm feeling happy
my face feels smiley and
everything in the world seems
especially wonderful.

Sometimes I laugh and laugh and laugh so much . . . my tummy hurts!

Laughing makes me feel *soooo* good.

There are many things that
make me feel happy – especially . . .
being with friends

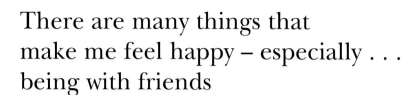

or baking cookies
with Grandma . . .

or when Dad takes me camping and
we sit around the camp-fire toasting marshmallows,
and talk and laugh and talk some more . . .

and gaze into the starry night . . .
and everything seems peaceful.

Feeling happy helps me to have more patience
and helps me not to get angry
over small problems . . .

and makes me feel more kind and caring
towards others.

Being happy can help someone
who is feeling sad or grouchy – feel better.
Helping someone feel happy
makes me feel really good.

Feeling happy is such a fantastic feeling.
It makes me feel good about the way I look
and the person I am.